This book belongs to:

....

....

Quarto is the authority on a wide range of topics.

Quarto educates, entertains and enriches the lives of
our readers—enthusiasts and lovers of hands-on living.

www.quartoknows.com

Publisher: Maxime Boucknooghe
Editorial Director: Victoria Garrard
Art Director: Miranda Snow
Designer: Victoria Kimonidou
Editor: Sophie Hallam

A NEW BURLINGTON BOOK

First published in the UK in 2016 by QED Publishing

Part of The Quarto Group
The Old Brewery
6 Blundell Street
London N7 9BH

A catalogue record for this book is available from
the British Library.

ISBN 978 1 78493 797 3

Printed in China

Hello, Mr Moon

Lorna Gutierrez

Illustrated by Laura Watkins

NEW BURLINGTON

Hello, Mr Moon.
You're looking full today,
unlike before you were
wasting away.

Are you taking
care of yourself?
You're **up**. You're **down**.
Why so skinny
and then so round?

Relax, little child. You will see, things happen that make me – ME!

It takes one year for Earth to get around the Sun –
365 days and its job is done!

Once a month I orbit, too –
but not around the Sun, just around you.

I'm lit by the Sun, that's why I seem bright –
you're seeing my sunlit side at night.

The movement of Earth, Sun and me
causes different phases…that's what you see!

But sometimes you're not there. Where'd you go? You disappear!

Sunlight is behind me – it's called my new moon.
It means you can't see me but you will soon!

I must admit, I enjoy less light –
it's easier for me to sneak around at night!

A sliver of light shows
my crescent moon lit.
The sunlight on me
is only a bit.

Half bright, Mr Moon, is something to see.
You're black and white – just like me!

That's my quarter moon, though some call it half.

See how I change as I follow my path?

Close to full, you shimmer
and shine, reflecting on my ocean
in a way that's so fine.

Now I'm gibbous, nearly all bright.
See me glimmer on your waters tonight.

Your light is so peaceful, it's really quite nice...

...shining brightly as I look for mice.

Full is my glory –
all eyes are on me!
I'm completely
lit and easy to see.

Yes, little cat, I do have some tricks like my brilliant, red, lunar eclipse.

Thanks, Mr Moon, we know you care,
even if we can't see you, you're still there!

New Moon

Crescent Moon

Quarter Moon

Gibbous Moon

Full Moon

Yes my friends, although I seem far,
I'll follow you, wherever you are.

Now night-time is over
and it's almost day,
it's time for other animals
to come out and play.

But remember, just
look **up** and I'll look **down**,
and know I'll always
be around.

Next Steps

- The moon circles around our Earth every month. This is called its orbit. Our planet Earth also orbits, but it orbits our Sun, which takes one year. Can the children find out what other planets are in our solar system?

- The moon appears brightly in the night sky because it reflects the light from the Sun. While the moon orbits, it waxes (gets bigger) or wanes (gets smaller) depending on where it is and what light we can see shining on the moon's surface.

- Every month, the moon completes a cycle, starting as a complete circle (at full moon), then shrinking until we can barely see it (at new moon). These stages are called the phases of the moon. Ask the children to draw a picture of all the different phases of the moon and label them.

- A lunar eclipse happens when the moon passes directly behind the Earth into its shadow. The Earth's shadow blocks sunlight but we can still see a red glow on the moon. Can the children find out when the next lunar eclipse is?

- In this story, the animals all have a relationship with the moon. Explain that the animals in the book are nocturnal, meaning that they are mainly active and awake at night. Ask the children what their favourite nocturnal animal is and see if you can find out more about it.

- The moon is very special. It gives us light at night and produces the ocean's tides. Lots of stories have been told about the moon and people have studied it for many centuries. Can the children find any more books to read about the moon?